In memory of My Dad ~ M·C·

For Lynn and Oberon ~ D·R·

LITTLE TIGER PRESS
An imprint of Magi Publications
1 The Coda Centre, 189 Munster Road, London SW6 6AW
www.littletigerpress.com
First published in Great Britain 2004
Text copyright © Michael Catchpool, 2004
Illustrations copyright © David Roberts, 2004
Michael Catchpool and David Roberts have asserted their rights
to be identified as the author and illustrator of this work under the
Copyright, Designs and Patents Act, 1988.
All rights reserved
ISBN 1 85430 867 X
A CIP catalogue record for this book is available from the British Library
Printed in Singapore by Tien Wah Press Pte.
2 4 6 8 10 9 7 5 3 1

Michael Catchpool

Hopping Mad!

illustrated by **David Roberts**

LITTLE TIGER PRESS
London

Fred lived next door to Finn.

Fred had five frogs and so did Finn.

One night when the moon was up and the grass
was damp, Finn's five frogs called to Fred's frogs,
"Come on over, we're having a party!"
"What an excellent idea!" Fred's frogs croaked back.
"We'll be right over!" and they hopped over the fence.

The frogs dived and splashed
and flipped and flopped and had
a fantastic time.

By the time the sun was coming up
they could hardly manage a hop.
"Phew!" croaked Fred's frogs.
"We really must be getting home,"
and they dragged themselves
back over the fence.

The next morning, as the sun sparkled on the water, Fred stood idly counting his frogs. "One, two, three, FOUR!"

Then he looked over the fence
and counted the frogs in Finn's pond.
"One, two, three, four, five, SIX!"
Fred was furious.

"Frog thief!" he shouted at Finn. "You should have five
frogs and you've got six. You've stolen one of mine!"
And Fred marched into Finn's garden and snatched
a frog before Finn could say a word.

"I'll soon put an end to your stealing!" shouted Fred, and with some wood and some nails he built his fence higher and higher.

That evening, as an owl swooped across the sky, Fred's five frogs called to Finn's five frogs, "Come over to our pond tonight for some fun."

"What an excellent idea!" croaked Finn's frogs.

The frogs frolicked and feasted on flies
until they were completely exhausted.
"Time to be getting home," they croaked.
Then Finn's frogs squeezed
back under the fence.

The next day, as the birds were singing
in the trees, Finn slowly counted his frogs,
"One, two, THREE!"

He glared over the fence into Fred's pond.
"One, two, three, four, five, six, SEVEN!"
Finn was fuming.

"Frog thief!" he shouted at Fred.
"You have seven frogs and I've only got three."
He marched right round to Fred's garden
and snatched back his two frogs.

"I'll stop you pinching my frogs!" said Finn,
and he dug a big, wide ditch by the fence.

That evening, while a hedgehog snuffled along
looking for worms, Finn's five frogs called to Fred's,
"Why not party in our pond tonight?"
So Fred's frogs scrambled over the huge fence
and leaped over the enormous ditch.

The frogs had a splendid time, diving and swimming,
dancing and singing until they could hardly croak.
Just before dawn, Fred's frogs returned home.
They leaped back over the enormous ditch
and scrambled back over the huge fence.

The following morning, while the dew
glistened on the grass, Fred carefully
counted his frogs.
"One, TWO!"

Then he counted the frogs in Finn's pond.
"One, two, three, four, five, six, seven, EIGHT!"
Fred was frantic.

"Frog thief!" he shouted at Finn.
"You've stolen three of my frogs," and he marched
through the gate and snatched back his frogs.

"I'll put a stop to this," Fred said,
and he put a great big cage right
over his frogs and his pond.

That evening, while a cat sat yowling on
the fence, Fred's five frogs called to Finn's frogs.
"We can't play tonight, we've been locked up."
"Then we'll come over to you," croaked Finn's frogs,
and they leaped across the great big ditch, over the
high fence and opened the door of the cage.

"Phew!" said Fred's frogs.
"You know, us frogs need our
freedom," and off they hopped,
with Finn's frogs close behind.

Now Fred has no frogs.
And neither does Finn.

But Fiona, who lives four doors down, has TEN!

Croak! Croak! Croak!